OFF WE GO!

Going to Buy Shoes

Avril Webster

Illustrated by David Ryley

Off We Go Publishing

Dedication
This series of books is dedicated to Stephen and Christia, the children who inspired its creation.

Acknowledgements
I would like to thank David Ryley, the artist for the series, whose talent, compassion and sense of humour is evident in all the illustrations.

I would also like to thank Stephen's speech & language therapist, his teachers and the mothers of his classmates for their contributions to these books.

Published by
Off We Go Publishing, 74 Salmon Weir, Annacotty, Co. Limerick, Ireland
www.offwego.ie

© Avril Webster, 2009

Printed in Ireland by KPM Print and Publishing Services

British Library Cataloguing in Publication Data

Webster, Avril.
    Going to buy shoes.
    1. Shoes - Purchasing - Pictorial works - Juvenile literature.
    I. Title II. Ryley, David.
    381.4'568531-dc22

ISBN: 978 1 906583 08 8

PRINT
IRISH

CLÓBHUAIL
IN ÉIRINN

My shoes are feeling tight.
We are going to buy new shoes.

We go to the shoe shop.

There are lots of shoes. I look at all the shoes.
Which ones do I like?

I sit and wait my turn.

The lady measures my feet.
My oh my! My feet have grown!

I like those shoes.
'Do you have them in my size?'

The lady gets the shoes.
She has the blue and red shoes in my size.

The lady feels where my toes and my heels
are in the new shoes.

I put on the new shoes. I walk around.
I look in the mirror.

Which shoes will I choose? I like the red shoes.
They feel good and look nice.

I have to pay. I give my money to the lady.
She puts my shoes in a bag.

'Bye bye, thank you.
See you next time.'

Hello from the Author

My name is Avril Webster and I am the author of this book. I am married to Robert and we have three children; Stephen, Michael and Rachel. Our eldest son Stephen has a moderate to severe intellectual disability (no specific diagnosis).

This book helps your child's:
* Confidence
* Self esteem
* Language development
* Communication skills

We feel passionately about including Stephen in our activities and everyday outings. Like many children with special needs, Stephen finds it difficult to cope with new experiences and changes to his routine.

We searched to find clear uncluttered books on everyday events, but we could not find any to suit Stephen's needs. With the help of teachers from Stephen's school, speech and language therapists and other mothers, I wrote this book and the other eleven in this series. (The list is on the back cover.)

Through Stephen's classmate Christia, I met the artist of the *Off We Go!* series, David Ryley. He has drawn the pictures for this book and also created the *Off We Go!* logo which features Stephen and Christia, the two special children that inspired the creation of these books!

We found that by preparing Stephen for an upcoming event or experience, he was not so scared and was able to get through it more easily. At the time of creating these books for Stephen, our daughter Rachel was at pre-school and we found they were helpful in explaining new events to her as well. Our other son, Michael was learning to read and he enjoyed reading the books independently.

We use this book in a number of ways:
* We read the book at home to prepare for the upcoming event/experience.
* We role play and play 'let's pretend' games using practical items from the home alongside the book to practise what is going to happen.
* We bring the book to the actual event and read it as we go through the event/experience.

Some re-occurring features in all the books are:

* Twelve clear pictures in a sequence (as advised by speech and language therapists).
* The same multi-ethnic characters are used in all books so the reader gets to know them.
* Where relevant, I have used a clock symbol to show a period of waiting or time up.

While reading and actively using this book with all our children, we have found that we have not only enjoyed the intimacy and power of reading together, but it has also improved **communication skills, language development and the children's confidence and self-esteem.**

The words used in these books are based on the actual words we use in our home. The speech and language therapist advised using language that Stephen would hear regularly. I have specifically used practical words to describe everyday events, to build vocabulary and support language development. Please change the words to the ones you would use in your home.

We use visual communication with Stephen all the time. We find using pictures essential for Stephen to understand what is happening. You can log on to my website www.offwego.ie for tips on how we use pictures and other ideas on preparing for new experiences.

Thank you for choosing this book and I hope you enjoy the others in the series too!

I hope it is as useful to you as it is in our family. I would love to hear from you so if you have any comments or thoughts, please e-mail me at avril@offwego.ie.

Best wishes,